Introduction

Optical illusions take advantage of basic weaknesses in the visual system. Playing with these illusions helps to sharpen your visual thinking skills. Would you like to know more?

Whenever you "see" an object, light rays are actually reflected from the object, past the protective outer cornea, and through a tiny opening called the pupil. The pupil is the dark spot in the middle of the iris. And the iris is the muscular disk that changes the size of the tiny opening, depending on the brightness of a scene. (The pigments in the iris determine your eye color!)

Behind the pupil and the iris is a lens that is so flexible that you can focus on near and far objects, and even see things that you're not really focusing on.

The light rays then pass through your jelly-like eyeball and onto the retina—a screen at the back of your eye. The retina is made up of little cellular structures called rods and cones, which are sensitive to light and color. From there, a pathway called the optic nerve relays the image to the brain.

Your brain interprets this information as a picture—ah, but not always "correctly"! There are no light-sensitive cells where the retina and optic nerve connect, creating a blind spot. And sometimes, the brain simply takes short cuts in processing information.

THE
LITTLE GIANT®BOOK
OF
Cool
Optical Illusions

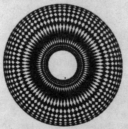

Gyles Brandreth, Michael A. DiSpezio,
Katherine Joyce, Charles H. Paraquin

Sterling Publishing Co., Inc.
New York

Material in this collection was adapted from *The World's Best Optical Illusions*, published in 1987 by Sterling Publishing Co., Inc.; first published under the title "Eye Teasers" © 1977 by Sterling Publishing Co., Inc. *The Great Book of Optical Illusions*, published in 1985 by Sterling Publishing Co., Inc.; first American edition published under the title "Seeing Is Not Believing" © 1980 by Sterling Publishing Co., Inc. *Visual Thinking Puzzles*, published by Sterling Publishing Co., Inc. © 1998 by Michael A. DiSpezio. *Optical Illusion Magic: Visual Tricks and Amusements*, first paperback edition published 2001 by Sterling Publishing Co., Inc. © 1999 by Michael A. DiSpezio. *Astounding Optical Illusions*, first paperback edition published in 1995 by Sterling Publishing Co., Inc. © 1994 by Katherine Joyce.

1 3 5 7 9 10 8 6 4 2

© 2002 by Sterling Publishing Co., Inc.
387 Park Avenue South, New York, NY 10016
Distributed in Canada by Sterling Publishing
c/o Canadian Manda Group, One Atlantic Avenue, Suite 105
Toronto, Ontario, Canada M6K 3E7
Distributed in Great Britain by Chrysalis Books
64 Brewery Road, London N7 9NT, England
Distributed in Australia by Capricorn Link (Australia) Pty. Ltd.
P.O. Box 704, Windsor, NSW 2756, Australia
Book design by StarGraphics Studio
Manufactured in China
All rights reserved

Sterling ISBN 1-4027-0521-2

SIDE-VIEW CROSS-SECTION OF THE EYE

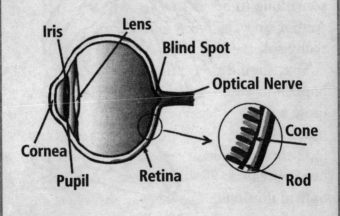

So, usually we see what we expect to see. But sometimes our perception lets us down, and we perceive something to be so that isn't really so!

That should happen to you quite a few times as you look through this book, because optical illusions very often manage to fool your perception. And then you begin to wonder—*is seeing really believing?!*

Now You See It ...

What's this?
An elegant vase or two old men?

8

Great Gaze

Gaze at the pattern on the facing page for at least a minute.

Quickly look at a perfectly blank wall and you'll find that you start seeing strange little moving specks on the wall.

Five Fields

Here are five fields.

Which is the largest and
which is the smallest in area?

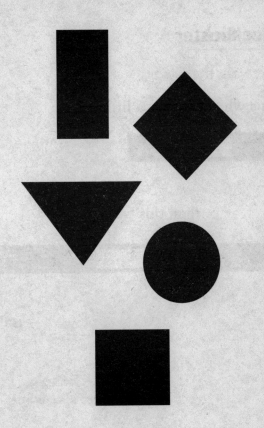

Blockbuster

This white block is a little bigger

than this white block

—isn't it?

Eye Teaser

Which line is bigger: **A** or **B**?

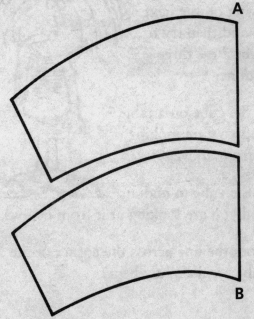

Curious Cube

Look carefully at the drawing on the next page and then try to answer these three questions:

1. Is the cube on a table and you are looking at it from above?

2. Is the cube in mid-air and you are looking at it from below?

3. Does the line across the corner of the cube seem slightly bent?

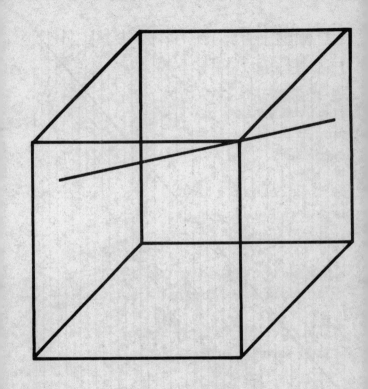

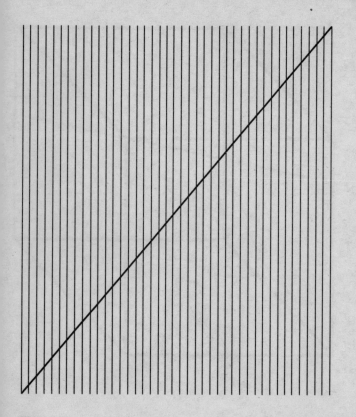

16

Ins and Outs

Look carefully at the diagonal
line on the facing page.

Is it straight? Or does it twist in and out of
the horizontal lines and seem a little jagged?

Around ...

Look at *either* the circle on this page or the next.

Concentrate on it and revolve the book. Turn it around and around as quickly as you can.

... and Around

When you stop, for a moment the pattern will suddenly seem to go in the opposite direction.

X Marks the Spot

Focus on the spot marked **X** and you will find that the dots in the square on the left appear in horizontal rows while the dots in the square on the right appear in vertical **columns**.

It will always happen that way—never the other way around!

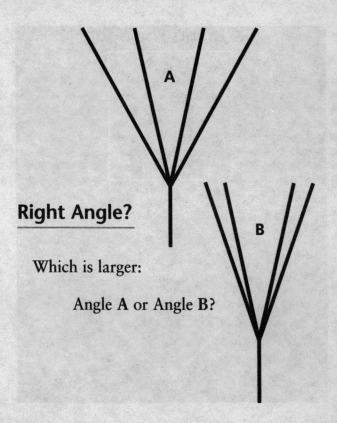

Right Angle?

Which is larger:

Angle A or Angle B?

Diamonds and Squares

Which is bigger:

The diamond or
the square?

Eye Dazzler

Look at the facing page for long enough
and your mind will really begin to boggle.

What can you see? Rows of triangles?
Rows of squares? Rows
of open boxes seen
from above? Or a
mixture of different
patterns that keep
changing as you look
at them?

25

Cog in the Middle

Holding the page flat in front of you, move the book in a circle clockwise. What happens to the outside circles? What happens to the cogwheel in the mid- dle?

Spinning Your Wheels

Examine the two sets of wheels below. In the top set, the steel shaft is attached at the same distance above each of the wheels. In the lower pair, the steel shaft is attached more toward the edge of the larger wheel.

If the small wheel spins in a clockwise direction, what will happen to the larger wheel? Will the motion of the larger wheel be different in the lower pair? If so, how?

Square World

Is one of these two areas
very slightly larger than the other?

Which one?

29

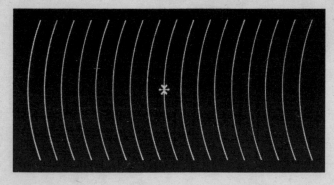

Watch 'em Bend!

Look at the star on this page steadily while you count to 100 very slowly.

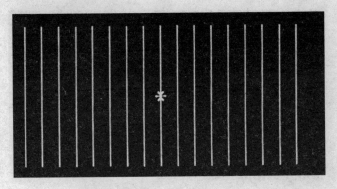

Now look at the star on *this* page and watch the lines curve in the opposite direction!

Impossible!

Look at the opposite page.

Whichever way you look at it, this is an "impossible" object.

That is, it is possible to *draw* it on paper, but you could never *build* it out of cardboard or wood.

If it looks perfectly all right to you, look again—starting at the base of the object and then letting your eye move up it.

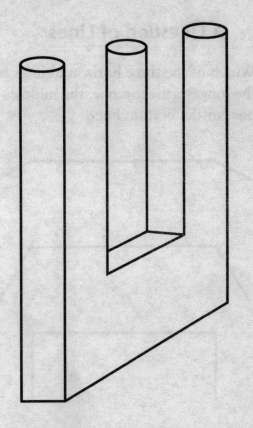

A Question of Lines

Which of the three horizontal lines is the longest: the top one, the middle one, or the bottom line?

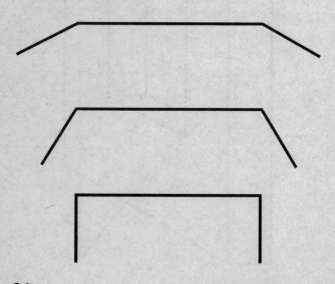

A Question of Angles

Which is the longer line:

the one from **A** to **C**
or
the one from **B** to **D**?

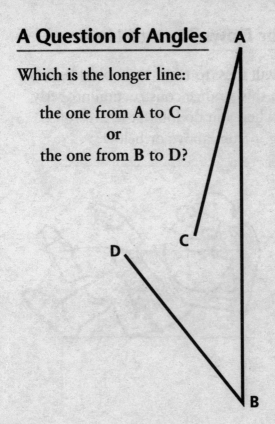

Up or Down?

You will have to turn the book sideways to see this strange construction properly. And when you do look at it, are you seeing it from above or below?

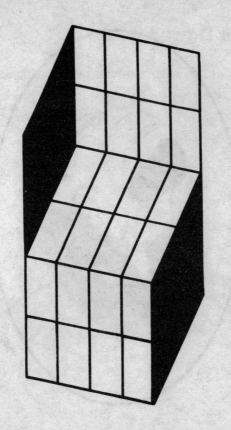

Portrait of a Lady

What can you see in this picture?

Is it a drawing of a very old lady?
Or is it a picture of a young woman with
her head turned slightly away from you?

Bull's-Eye

Revolve these pages, and the spirals will seem to get bigger or smaller, depending upon in which direction you are turning the book.

Center Point

Glance at the facing page
and tell what you can see
right in the very middle of it.

12
ABC
14

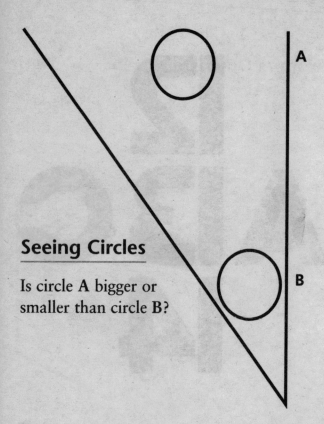

A

Seeing Circles

Is circle A bigger or
smaller than circle B?

B

Upstairs Downstairs

Find the top step. When (and if) you find it, start looking for the bottom step!

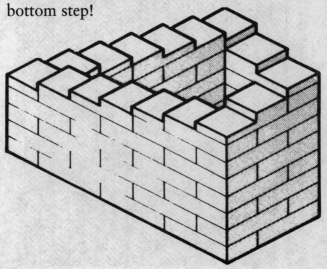

46

The Skinny Shimmy

How many of the vertical lines on the facing page are bending this way and that? And how many of them are perfectly straight?

How Far This Time?

Is the distance between A and B greater or smaller than the distance between C and D?

A

B

C

D

Master Carpenter

Ask some friends if they can build this
hollow crate for you from 12 pieces
of wood. Tell them they can have
$1,000 if they
succeed!

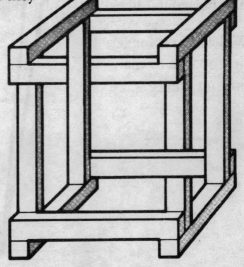

Point of View

Look carefully at the two horizontal lines.

Which one is longer: the top one or the bottom one?

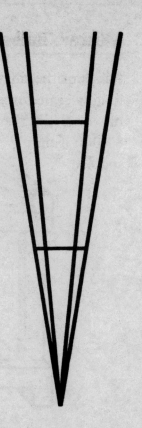

A Curve Ball

Which of the three arcs is the biggest:

> the top one,
> > the middle one,
> > > or the bottom one?

From Here to There

Is the line from **A** to **B** longer

or shorter than the line from C to D?

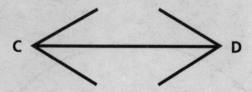

Where Are You?

Are you up in the sky looking down on the roof of a house? Or are you in a room looking into a corner?

Which End Is Up?

Here's an unusual tube. Look carefully at it for at least a minute and then

decide if you are looking down the tube from above it or up the tube from under it.

Countdown

How many cubes can you count here?

And if you found that mind-boggling,
you can really get yourself confused
by trying to find
your way through
the cube maze.
Using tracing
paper, go in at one
arrow and come out
the other.

Great or Small?

Which of the two circles is the larger?

The one on this page?

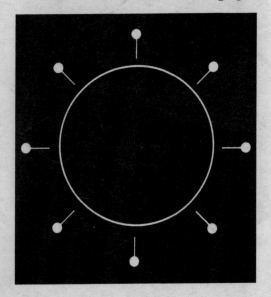

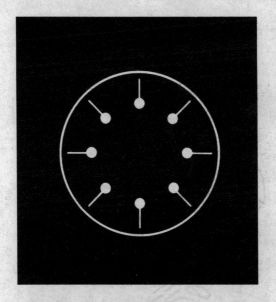

Or the one on this page?

Crisscross

Glance at the facing page and strange gray spots will appear at all the points where the lines cross. Look at any one crossing in particular and the gray spot that was there will suddenly disappear!

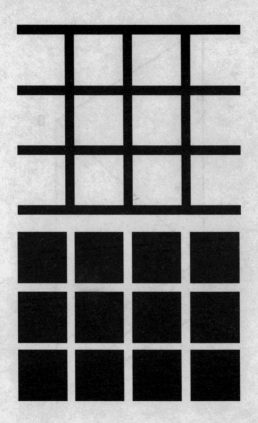

61

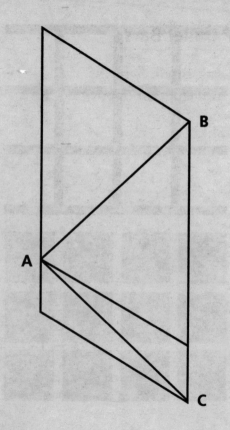

Parallel Bars

Look carefully at the
parallelogram opposite.

Which line is longer:
AB or AC?

Strange Circles

Which of the three rings is a perfect circle?

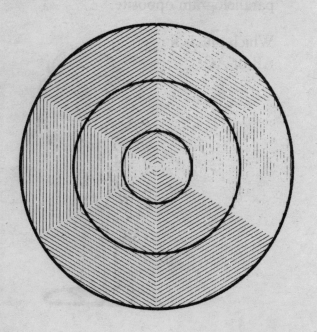

Topsy Turvy

Look carefully at this picture by the great Dutch artist Verbeek—then turn it upside down and give yourself a surprise.

The largest of the Rocs picks her up by the skirt.

Just as he reaches a small grassy point of land, another fish attacks him, lashing furiously with his tail.

Fair and Square

Of the three squares, which
one is the smallest?

68

Turn, Turn, Turn

Look at the circle on the opposite page and keep looking at it.

As you look at it, it will seem to revolve. (Don't look at it for too long, or you might begin to feel a little dizzy!)

Puzzling Pages

A blast of wind has separated the pages of a local newspaper. From the page numbers shown below can you determine how many pages were in the complete newspaper?

Honeycomb

Look at this pattern long enough and you'll find the circles begin to look like hexagons!

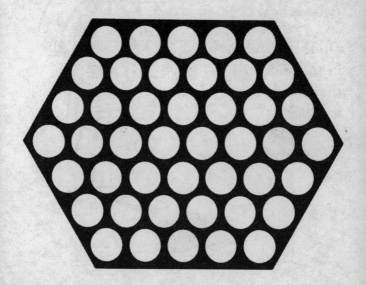

Curvy Lines

Look carefully at the
two vertical lines.

Do they bend outward
in the middle? Do
they bend inward in the
middle?

Stair Case

Look at these stairs any way you like and you'll still feel you could climb them. Whether you look at the page as it is, turn it sideways, or turn it upside down—you'll still find stairs to climb.

This amazing image is a maze as well as an eye-teaser! Using tracing paper, go in at one arrow and see how long it takes you to come out at the other arrow.

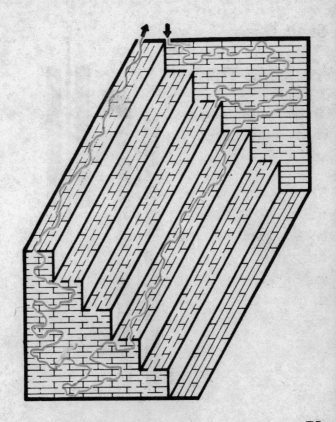

Thick and Thin

Of the two thin lines,
which is the longer?

Wooden Triangle

If you're any good at carpentry, try
making this simple wooden triangle.

Squaring the Circle

Which of the two circles is the larger?

A

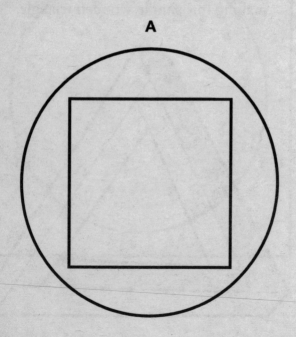

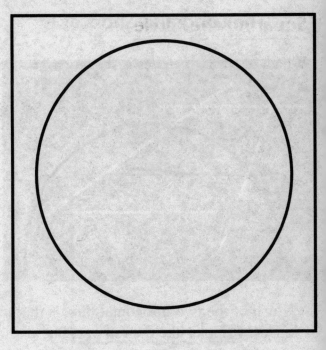

B

The Long and Short of It

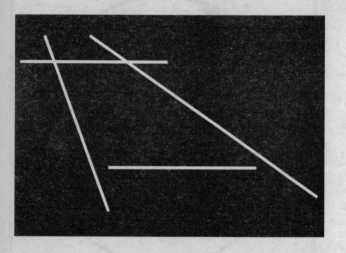

Which of the two horizontal lines is the longer? It looks like the top one, but are you **sure**?

"E" Is for Eye-Popping

Is this letter "E" toppling forward or sinking down? Look at it steadily for half a minute.

Outstanding Hat

Here's a high hat. How much greater is its height than its width?

It's also an amazing maze! Use tracing paper and try to draw a path from one arrow to the other.

Woodshop Dilemma

A practical-looking construction.
Can you build it?

Straphanger Siblings

These are twin brothers, but one of them has a bigger appetite. Which one?

A Question of Balance

Is this cube higher and wider in the back than in the front?

The Hole Truth

John P. Cubic was placed on the witness stand to be questioned about his puzzle-

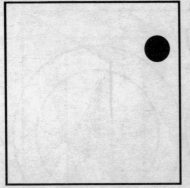

solving abilities. Of course, he declared himself a skilled puzzle-ologist. To prove it, he presented a cardboard square with an off-center hole.

Cubic claimed that by cutting this cardboard into only two pieces, he could move the hole into the center of this square. Can you figure out his cutting pattern?

Inside Outside

Is the outside circle of A smaller than the inside circle of B?

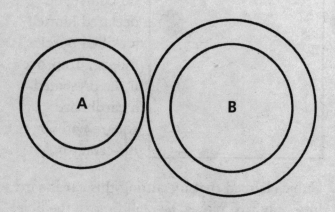

Popcorn, Anyone?

Which of these movie-goers
is the tallest?

Lots of Dots

In this crowd of dots, there are five in the shape of a cross. Can you pick them out?

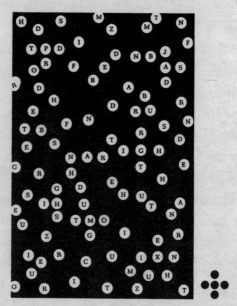

Secrets of Ancient Greece

The beautiful temple architecture of Greek antiquity, which seems so flawless and symmetrical, looks that way only with the help of some shrewd visual tricks.

The people of Greece made the roof and the base (the horizontal lines) of their buildings look straight by curving them upward in the middle, with edges turned toward the ground. If they had actually left the horizontal lines straight, the line would seem to sag in the middle.

The ancient architects also adjusted the buildings' columns (the vertical lines) in several ways. For example, because vertical lines seem thinner in the middle than at the ends, the columns were built with a little bulge in the center.

Greek columns lean together just a few degrees at the top—otherwise, they would seem to spread out as they went up. And, if you measured the temples' colonnades and arcades, you would find that the distance between the columns varies. This too, was not an accident.

Bright colors placed in front of darker colors seem wider than they do when placed against a light background. Therefore, the columns in front of shadowy areas would seem much wider—and so, this was taken into account.

The building designers of Greece knew all about optical illusions, and they used them to create the *illusion* of symmetry and perfection!

What is
the matter
with these
columns?

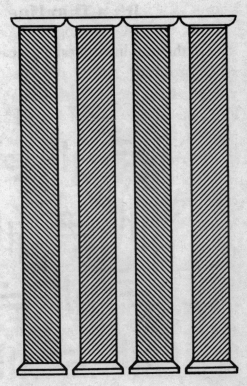

It's a Thin Line

Are the thin lines parallel to each other?
Or crooked?

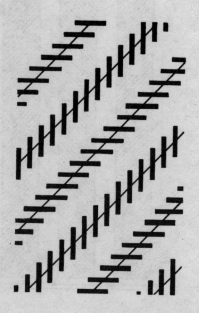

Straight and Narrow?

Are the vertical lines straight?

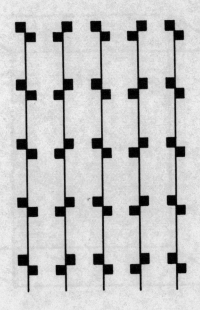

About Face

Which side of this cube is in front, and which is in back? Look at it steadily.

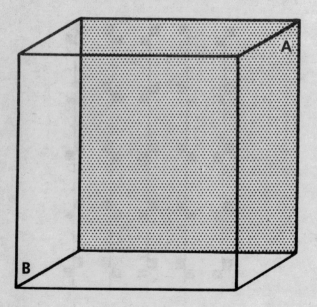

How Do *You* See It?

Are these five rooftops of connected houses?
Or is this a 10-part folding screen?

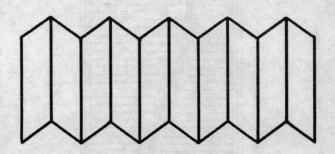

The Highs and Lows

Is the left side of this picture high, or the right side?

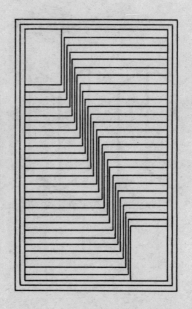

Count the Cubes

Are there seven cubes here, or eight?

What Is This?

Are you looking inside a tube?
Or at the top of a beach ball?

View of a Room

But a very strange room.
Are we inside it—or outside?

Investigate This

Each of these detectives obviously enjoys wearing a different style of hat. But which detective has the largest mouth?

A

B

C

D

Clips and Pins

Which is the longest object in this picture?

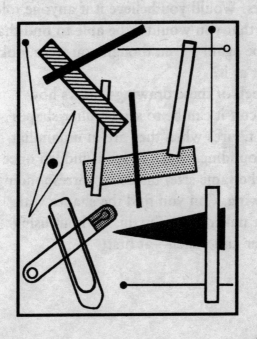

Hidden Shapes

Take a look at each shape on the following pages. Would you believe it if anyone told you that you wouldn't be able to find that shape again—even though you were looking right at it?

Each of these drawings shows how difficult it can be to see familiar shapes and figures when they are in unfamiliar surroundings. Each shape is hidden once (at the same size) inside its corresponding drawing. Can you find the shapes with your naked eye? Try this without using paper and pencil—at first!

Shape A

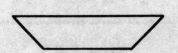

Drawing A

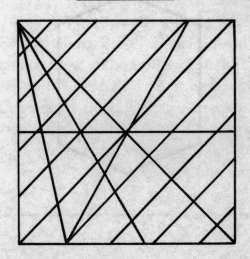

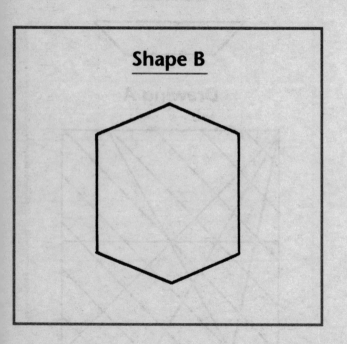

Shape B

Drawing B

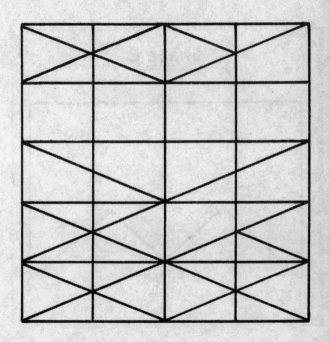

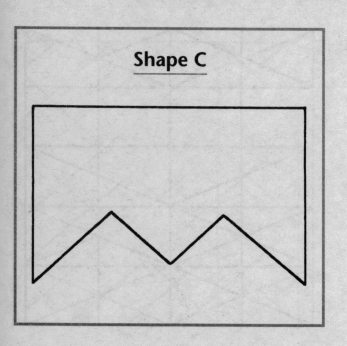

Shape C

Drawing C

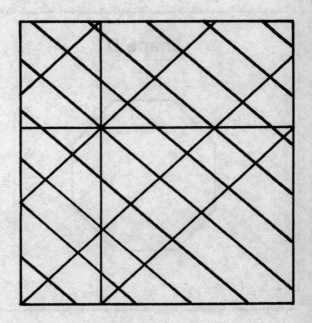

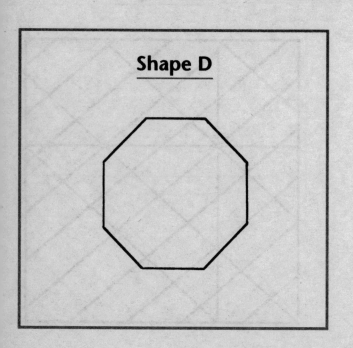

Shape D

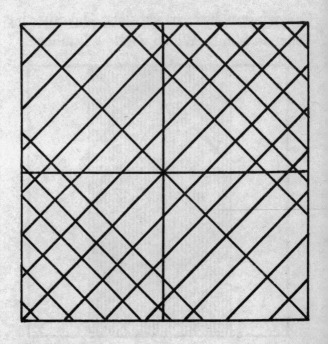

A Decorator's Dilemma, Maybe!

One window has vertical slats. The other has Venetian blinds. Which window is taller ...

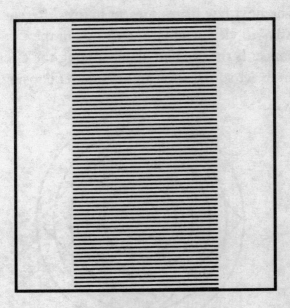

... and which is wider?

Square Dancing

The next few pages present many different ways to view a square. Step one in the dance: Is the angular shape among the circles an exact square—or are its sides collapsing?

Are the horizontal lines
parallel to each other?

What is happening to the diamond shape?

Is this a perfect square?

Are the sides of this square bulging out?

Are the sides of this one caving in?

How many squares are there
in the drawings on these two pages?

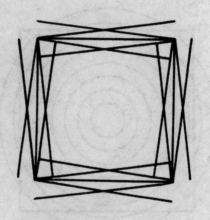

Circle Surrounded

What is the matter with this circle?

Flat-top or Buzz Cut?

Isn't this circle flat at the top?

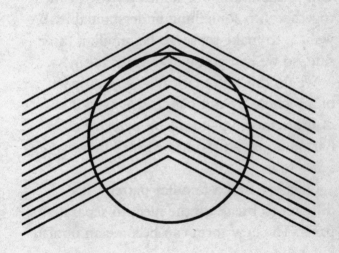

Seeing Isn't Everything

After the light impressions are gathered and sent to the brain, our minds try to put them together into something understandable. We want it to make sense, to be familiar, to be safe, so we can go on about our business.

We do this automatically—even if parts of a picture are not connected, even if parts of it are missing!—until we perceive a harmonious, satisfying "whole" that makes sense to us.

Once we find a familiar pattern, it's difficult to break up the idea, to separate its parts. The new form can become an optical illusion—such as those shown on the next few pages. We can't concentrate on just part of it because our imaginations keep putting back what we try to block out of our minds!

For the first puzzle in this section, take a look at these circles:

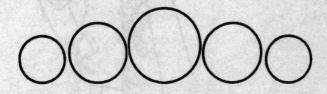

Do they sit on level ground, or do they arch upward?

Although parts of this
picture are missing,
our imaginations
   draw them in.

What white shape seems to be placed in front of the square?

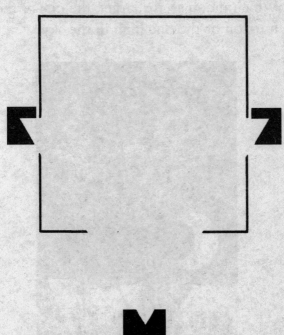

How High the Moon

Which moon seems larger, the one at the horizon or the one high in the sky?

Circular Logic

The puzzles on the next few pages all involve circles. To start, which inner circle is larger—the one on this page ...

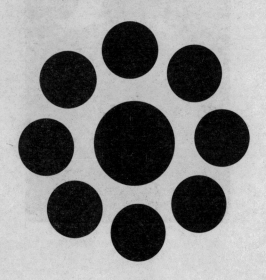

... or the inner circle on this page?

Which circle is the largest?

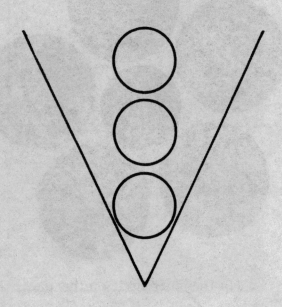

Which of these circles are the same size, those in row A or those in row B?

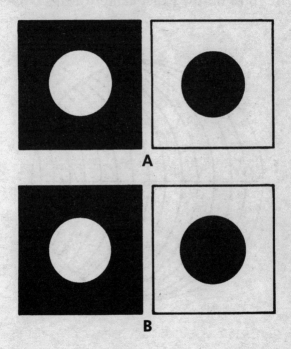

A

B

Can you find the exact center of this circle?

Afterimages

After you concentrate on a picture for a while your eyes get tired. The most tired parts are certain spots on the retina, the part of the eye that contains light-sensitive cells. The brightest tones cause the greatest stress to these cells, which gradually become less sensitive to light.

When you look away from the picture and focus on a sheet of blank white paper, the nerve ends that are less tired will lightly reproduce the darker sections of the picture. Your eye transforms a negative into a positive!

You can check out afterimages and other similar effects in the puzzles on the following pages ...

What shows up on the intersecting white lines, even though they are all white?

Concentrate for a while on the slanting lines. Then shift to the vertical lines. What do you see?

What do you see when you focus on the black lines where they cross each other?

The spoke-wheel phenomenon: If you rotate this or look at it steadily, what do you see?

Concentrate very hard on a point in the white field of intersecting lines for about 30 seconds, then quickly shift your attention to one of the black squares. What do you see inside the black squares?

What is the matter with these triangles?

Will the single square at the top left fit into the black space between the two squares at the bottom—and between the two on the right?

Are the white bars
straight or do they
bulge and bend?

Are these pointed arches continuous or broken?

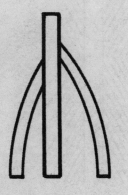 

Are the vertical lines straight? Do the short, slanted lines go straight through them—or is their pattern broken up?

Turn this page in a circle clockwise. Then turn it in a circle counterclockwise. Is there a difference, beside just their direction?

Little Things Mean a Lot

The first thing we see in any picture is usually the most obvious, most striking part. We often overlook smaller things, even though they may hold the key to a more important pattern.

The designs on the next five pages have been put together from geometric forms. For example, this pattern  has been created from this shape

Can you tell which simple shape forms the basis for the other patterns?

149

150

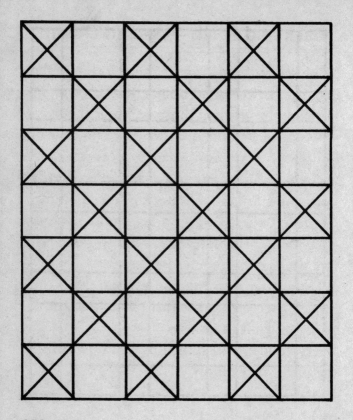

152

Back and Forth—Up and Down

Some scientists say it is "easier" to figure the distance between two points that lie on a horizontal level than those on vertical lines.

We can guess the distance from house to house, for example, or tree to tree—far more accurately than the distance between a house and a plane that just appeared on the horizon. Others say we've had more experience with horizontal distances and there is less we have to take into account.

Usually we overestimate vertical distances, even if they are just printed on the paper in front of us.

Try your eye on some ups and downs in the pages that follow ...

How does height (H) correspond in size with width (W)?

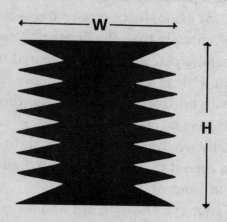

Is the dot midway between the point and the base of this triangle—or is it too high up?

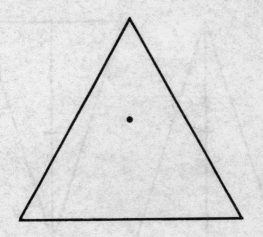

Are the crossbars exactly in the middle of the center line of these triangles?

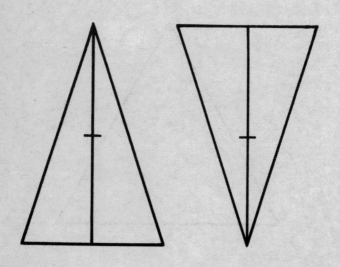

Is **A** larger than **B**?

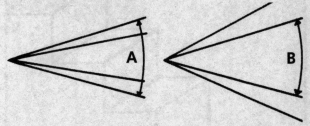

A normal staircase?
Try walking on it upside down!

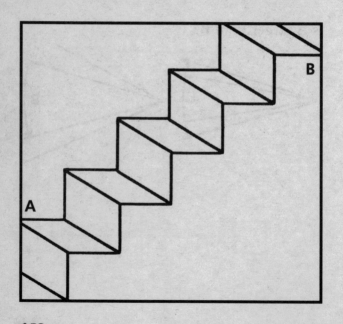

Which lines are the same length?

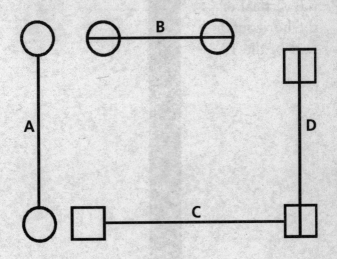

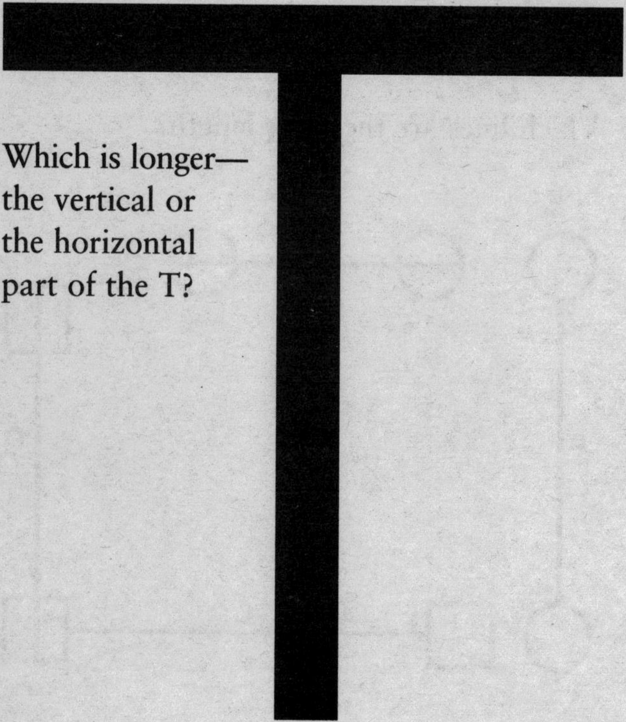

Which is longer—
the vertical or
the horizontal
part of the T?

How does the height of this top hat (A-B) compare with the width of its brim (C-D)?

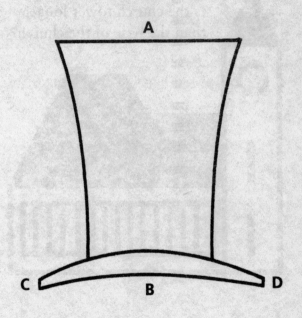

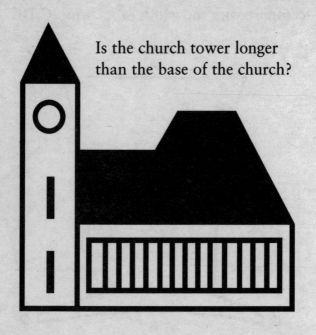

Is the church tower longer than the base of the church?

Which figure has the longest sides?

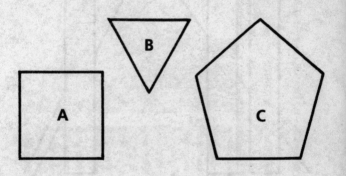

In the left-hand figure, is the diagonal line straight? In the right-hand figure, which line is the continuation of A? Is it B, or is it C?

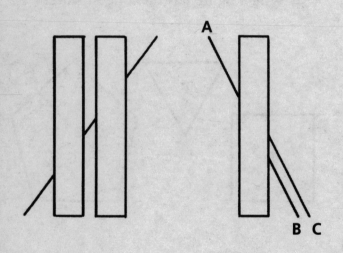

Which is longer, line **A** or line **B**?

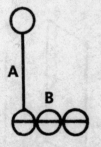
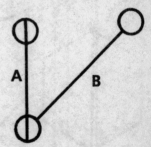

Is the center line **A** shorter than ...

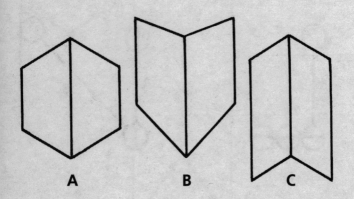

A   B   C

... the other center lines in **B** through **F**?

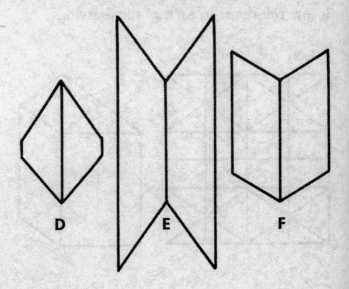

More Hidden Shapes

On the following pages you'll find more puzzles with hidden shapes! Can you locate the shape in each of the drawings?

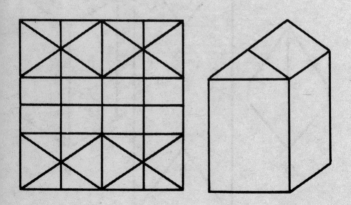

170

A Star in the Firmament

This star is hidden among the designs
in the drawing on the facing page.
Where is it hiding?

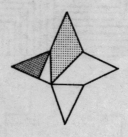

173

Curves Ahead!

Watch out for the curves coming up! Can you navigate the following pages and answer these questions correctly?

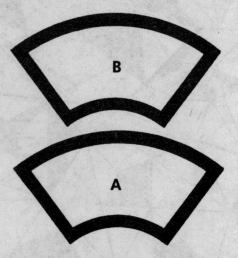

Are A and B the same size?

Are the lined-in sections (**B**) of the circle larger than the open sections (**A**)?

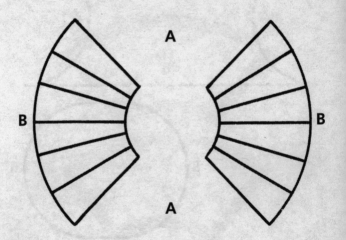

Is A-to-A the same length as B-to-B?

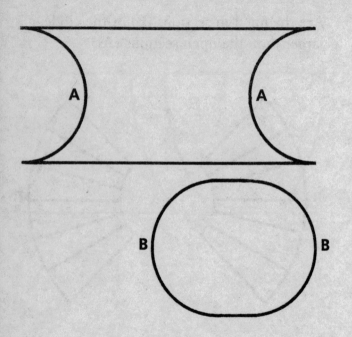

Which glass has a wider base?

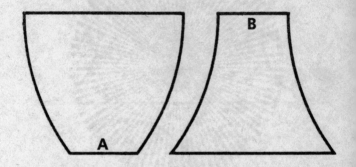

Cosmic Flower

Take a look at the way this design pulsates. This is why: When you look at anything that is close to you, the muscles around your eyes pull into a spherical shape to get the words and pictures in focus. But because the lens of your eye isn't perfectly round, some parts of what you're looking at will be in focus and others will look blurry.

Normally, these differences in the clarity of your vision are on the outer edge of the object you're looking at, so you can still read the words and recognize the pictures. But in an illusion such as this one—where all the lines come from different angles and meet at the center—it is impossible for you to focus clearly on all of it at once.

Your eyes are always making tiny movements that you cannot prevent, no matter how hard you try. So the clear parts of the design and the blurry parts are constantly changing. This is called "optical distortion," and it's what makes the picture seem to move, shimmer, swirl or pulsate!

Shimmering Squares

The shimmering effect you see in this
illusion is caused by optical distortion.

This illusion is unusual because all the lines in it are sloped forward 45° or backward 135° degrees. Try the following experiment to see why this helps make the illusion interesting:

Concentrate on one of the rows of lines that are sloped at 45°. You'll find that all the squares formed by these lines appear steady, while the squares formed by lines sloping backward at 135° look blurry and faint, and seem to shimmer.

Then concentrate on a row of lines sloped at 135° and you'll see that all the squares formed with lines sloped at 45° will look blurry and seem to shimmer. This effect occurs because your eyes cannot focus on all of the illusion at once. The parts that you do focus on will appear clear, while the other parts will look blurry.

All Square

This optical illusion is especially puzzling. If you study it closely, the ovals in the middle first seem to bulge out and then seem to recede.

The reason they change is that when your eyes scan the design from left to right, the position of the ovals suggests to your brain that the ovals are popping out. But then your eyes go back over the picture.

With so many different ways to scan the illusion—and no clues to which way is "right"—you may see the ovals recede or do any number of other interesting tricks.

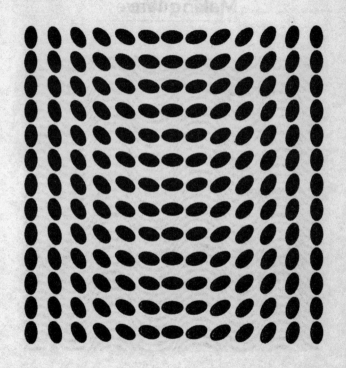

183

Making Waves

When you stare at this optical illusion for a while the curved lines seem to form the crests and valleys of the waves. They may even seem to move a little.

If you stare some more—until your eyes get tired—you may also see phantom lines of color (especially in bright light) where the curved lines run parallel to each other, between the valleys and crests of the waves.

The restless motion of the waves in this illusion is caused by optical distortion.

Jester

If you look at this circular checkerboard closely, it will seem to pulsate and shimmer. You may also see the black-and-white patches line up to form petals of a flower.

The shimmering is caused by optical distortion. But the petals formed by your brain are an example of another phenomenon called "good continuation."

This happens because your brain is trying to make sense out of what it sees. It seeks out shapes or patterns that it recognizes. Sometimes it works so hard and so cleverly that it imagines an object that isn't really there.

And then we have an optical illusion!

Net Working

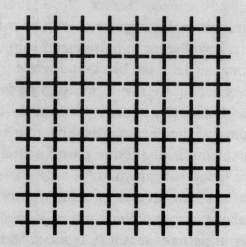

In this neat illusion, tiny white dots appear to join together to form phantom white crosses. This is another example of your brain trying to make sense of the visual information it is receiving—good continuation.

You can also see tiny gray dots in the center of the black crosses. Why? Special cells in your visual system respond strongly to small patches of light and dark.

If a small light patch is surrounded by more light, these cells will not respond so strongly to the small patch of light in the middle. If a small dark patch is surrounded by more darkness, these cells will not respond so strongly to the small patch of dark in the middle. So, in the case of the black crosses, your visual system does not respond fully to the middle of them and you see them as gray instead.

You can force your eyes and brain not to "overlook" the midpoint of the crosses, however. If you focus your attention fully upon one cross at a time, you will be able to see it as an ordinary black cross.

Tricky Tiles

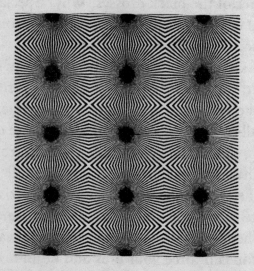

What makes this design vibrate? Right! It's optical distortion again. The repetition of the same design on each tile helps to make this illusion even more effective.

Zinnia

Here you may see some gray or white spots at the points where the black lines meet. This is caused by your eyes' response to dark and light. You may also see that the imaginary dots "link up" to form a series of circles that radiate out from the middle of the illusion—another example of good continuation!

Lattice

This illusion is an example of the role that contrast plays in your perceptions.

Although there are only two colors used in this design—black and white—the tiny white dots in the middle, where the black lines intersect, seem brighter and whiter than the larger white squares.

That's because the tiny white squares are more completely surrounded by the black lines than the larger white squares.

193

Square's Square

This illusion may remind you of "Shimmering Squares," in which lines drawn at different angles confuse the brain. The squares here that have been drawn on the background pattern may look as if they have been bent, but in fact they are perfectly straight!

This is an example of the "Zollner effect," which shows how straight lines appear to bend if they intersect with or are seen against a background of curved lines or lines drawn at different angles.

This strange effect occurs because your eyes and brain work together to try to make the straight lines fit into the background pattern.

195

Spiral Square-Case

The squares in the foreground look as if they are bent, right? However, this is another example of the Zollner effect.

If you hold a ruler alongside them, you'll see that the lines in the square are just as straight as they can be. It's only the curves of the spiral background that make the square seem bent.

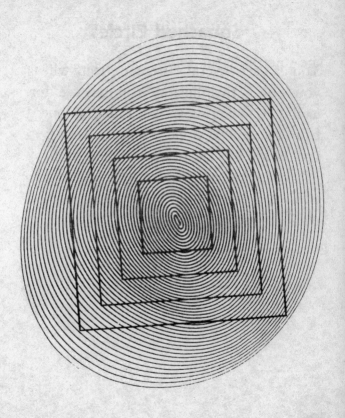

Squashed Circles

You can see several different effects when you look at this illusion. You may see, for example, flickering spokes radiating out from the central circle. Those flickering spokes are a result of optical distortion.

You could also view the smallest circle in two ways—as the top of a cone or as the end of a funnel!

Seasick Circle

If you watch this drawing while you turn
the book around in a circle, you will be
able to see a series of spirals moving up
and down in three dimensions.

This is called a "stereokinetic effect," and it's the result of a complex series of inter-actions between your eyes and your brain.

When this design rotates, the images sent to your brain are constantly changing. Because each circle is drawn with lines that vary in thickness, there is no stable point in the illusion for you to focus on. This is con-fusing to your brain, which likes to make orderly patterns out of what you see. So your brain looks for another pattern and sees that some of the curved lines seem to link up to form a spiral. As the curves that form the spiral rotate and change position, each of your eyes simultaneously sends your brain a slightly different image. When your brain puts this all together, it decides that it must be seeing a spiral moving up and down.

The Escalator

When you look closely at this illusion, you may get the impression that the horizontal panels are moving—with a tiny jerking motion—and the central panel may seem to be unexpectedly bright.

The reason that the "Escalator" seems to move is that you can't keep your eyes perfectly still, no matter how hard you try, and as your eyes move about, so does the image in the illusion!

Chrysanthemum

When you look at this design, you get the impression that it is not flat, but three-dimensional. Some parts of the illusion appear higher, and some lower—which gives the impression of depth.

However, if you look at the curved lines that define the bumps and hollows of the flower, you will find a curious situation: Look at the curve that defines the outer edge of the flower and follow it right around the circle. In some places the curved lines seem to define a hump, and at others a hollow.

This object could not exist in three dimensions. Along with being another shimmering example of optical distortion, "Chrysanthemum" is an example of an impossible figure.

The Temple

This is a reversing figure that can be looked at as a pyramid viewed from above, with the smallest square forming the top—or as a passageway leading toward a tiny square door. If you look steadily at this illusion, you will probably see it flash between these two images!

Hidden Pictures

The picture puzzles in this section come from *Cole's Funny Picture Book*, by Edward William Cole and published in the 1800s. Cole's book contains all sorts of stories, rhymes and pictures. But the most interesting things in the book are the picture puzzles—the best of which are reprinted here.

These pictures may look ordinary, but they're really great examples of the art of illusion. If you didn't know that there were pictures hidden inside the pictures, you'd probably never know what you were missing.

In this picture, for example, some wild
animals have gotten loose. Where is
the bear?

He's up in the tree!

This is an easy one. For the rest of these puzzles, you'll usually need to turn the book around and examine the scene closely. So, look sharp and see how many hidden faces, animals, and people you can find! If you get totally stuck, the answers are in the back of this book.

Here is the showman and his learned dog.
Where is his wife?

Here are the rats. Where is the cat?

Here is Bluebeard and his wife.
Where is their donkey?

There's a lot of furniture in this room,
but where is the cup?

This road leads up to the giant's castle.
Where is the giant?

Old Mother Hubbard is resting comfortably in her shoe. Where is her landlord?

Her dog has startled poor Mother Hubbard.
Where is her butler?

Mother Hubbard is serving tea to her
children, but five of them are missing.
Can you find them?

The rats are hiding from this cat. Can you find where they have gone?

This is a faithful Newfoundland dog, but where, oh where, is his master?

Can you find Captain Webb in this view
of Niagara Falls?

The queen
is searching
everywhere.
Will she ever
find the king?

You can plainly see the goat. Now find the
milkmaid.

Here is the cook
preparing a stew.
But where is the
rabbit he plans to
serve for dinner?

Everyone's down by the seashore—except the bird. Can you find it?

Visual Thinking

Visual thinking uses the incredible power of your "mind's eye" to define the way we process all sorts of information. Visual thinking isn't stuck in the present. We can use it to reflect back into the past—and it can just as easily jump into the future.

The next puzzles are mind-bending challenges developed to test your visual thinking skills. Open your eyes, and your mind, and have fun!

Let's get warmed up with this verbal puzzle: Six people attended a gala for visual thinkers. If all guests shook hands with everyone else, and no pair shook hands more than once, how many handshaking events were there?

Pie Pieces

There are many skills we associate with visual thinking. Some of these skills may be more difficult to master than others. For example, the ability to mentally rotate objects is often harder than we might imagine.

Try this: If you were to assemble the pieces on the facing page into a circle, what would the figure formed by the inner lines look like?

Link Latch

While digging through a box of metal links, a jeweler uncovers the three joined links shown on the facing page. She decides to separate the links and begins to examine them.

After handling them for a while, she discovers a way to disconnect all three by opening just a single link! Can you do the same thing?

Code Caper

What animal is represented in the code below?

Hint: From our earliest years, we learn to identify objects by the space they occupy. Artists, however, sometimes use the space that doesn't occupy something. It's called negative space and is the fabric that surrounds things. A bit of negative space might help you solve this puzzle.

Troubling Tree

Can you discover the pattern in this "tree" and use it to solve the missing number?

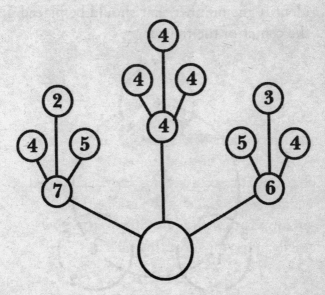

The Circle Game

Can you determine the pattern in the figure below? If so, use what you've discovered to identify the number that should be placed in the center of the figure.

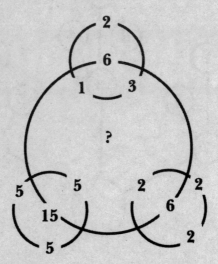

What's Next?

Complete the sequence.

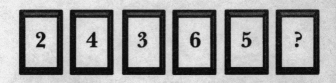

Sink Your Teeth

Both cog **A** and cog **D** have 60 teeth—but
cog **B** has 30 teeth, and cog **C** has 10 teeth.
Suppose cog **B** makes 20 complete turns
every minute. Which will spin faster, cog **A**
or cog **D**?

Hands On

Carefully examine each of these hands. Then decide which one of the nine hands is unlike all the others.

Mirror Madness

Do you realize that your brain is constantly trying to make sense of the information sent to it by your eyes?

As you may already know, the image that falls upon the retina of your eye is upside down. Your brain, however, flips the image over into a more logical upright appearance. Use that talent to answer this riddle: "Mirror, mirror, on the wall, which of the choices, **A** through **D**, is a reflection of the larger tile?"

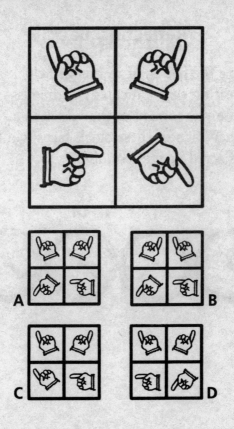

Reflecting Back

Imagine the hands of a standard clock in the position that indicates the time is 4:20. Suppose you looked at that clock in a mirror. Which of these clock faces would the reflected image resemble?

I   II   III   IV

OK, let's make it a bit more challenging. Suppose that the hands of a clock indicate the time is 2:40. Suppose you turned the clock upside down and then looked at its mirror reflection. Which one of these faces would the reflected image resemble?

I   II   III   IV

Spacing Out

Let's leave the eye-brain puzzles for a moment and just "space out."

A shuttle astronaut leaves her craft to work on a disabled satellite. She lands on one corner of the satellite (which is a perfect cube) and realizes that she must walk across the satellite's surface to the opposite corner. To conserve oxygen, she must follow the shortest possible route.

Is her planned route—identified by the dotted line—the shortest path between opposite corners?

241

Out-of-this-World Construction

Orbiting above the earth are four cubic sections of a soon-to-be-constructed space station. Astronauts will assemble the four separate cubes into a four-cube station.

The only problem is that the astronauts left the construction plans back on earth! Your job is to determine how many different four-cube arrangements are possible—if the cubes can only be joined squarely and face-to-face.

Sector Sever

Four alien civilizations are dividing up the universe, when they encounter a sector of space that has this unique arrangement of planets.

If all four civilizations are to get identical sectors of space—with each sector containing three different planets—how should this region be divided?

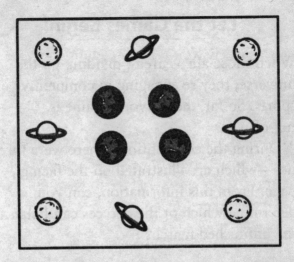

Let the Games Begin!

When those aliens aren't dividing up the universe, they're engaging in competitive sports. So far, their favorite game is tug-of-war.

During the competitions, there were three ties—which are illustrated on the facing page. From this information, can you determine which of the choices can balance the unfinished match?

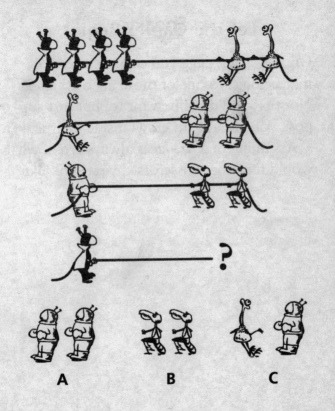

A   B   C

Sneaky

On the facing page you can see a sneaker that belongs to one of those alien athletes. Not that you'd really want to, but just suppose you are able to crawl inside the sneaker.

Assuming that the laces always cross, what would the inner crisscrossed view look like?

Spiral Bound

An astrologer photographs two side-by-side spiral galaxies. When she examines her files, however, she discovers that one of the photos is of a different galaxy pair.

Examine the six images on the facing page. One pair is unlike the others. Can you identify the different image?

A   B   C

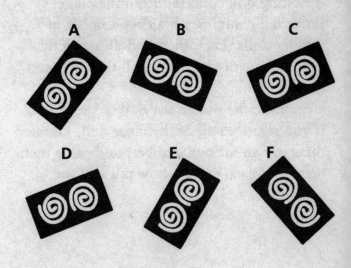

D   E   F

Nesting Dolls

A nesting doll collected from the planet *Infinitum* contains a limitless number of smaller dolls. Each smaller doll is exactly half the size of the larger doll that it "nests" within.

Suppose the outermost doll is 1 foot tall. If you removed all of the inner dolls (assume there are an infinite number) and place them on top of each other—how tall will the stack rise?

Naughty Notes

And now, a musical distraction ... Which pair of notes is unlike the other six pairs?

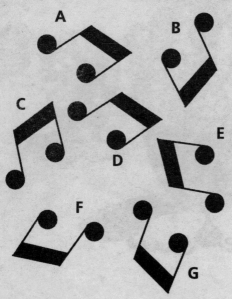

Pencil Stack

Which is the third pencil up from the bottom of the stack?

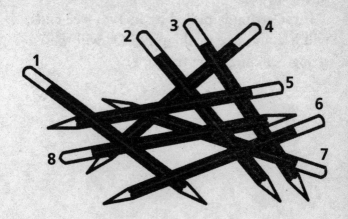

Amaze-ing String

Shown on the facing page is an odd loop of string, with a pipe located at the center of the string.

If the string is pulled by its two free ends, will it come free of the pipe? Or will the string get caught by the pipe?

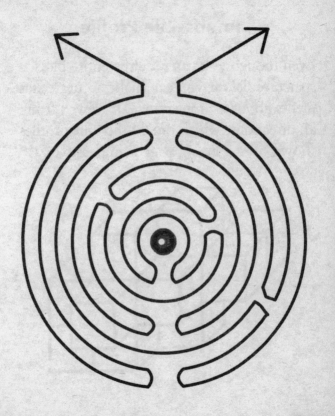

Impossible Profile

Even though you can't see the entire block structure below, you can make accurate statements about its appearance. If viewed from all directions, which one of the four profiles shown on the facing page is impossible?

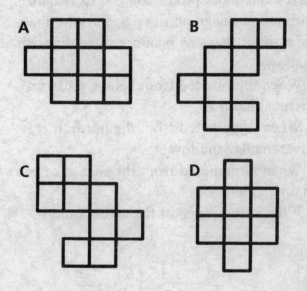

Only the Shadow Knows

Here's one more puzzle for you to visualize without an image on the page: Try to imagine a shape that can produce three different shadows.

When illuminated from below, it casts a circular shadow.

When illuminated from the north, it casts a rectangular shadow.

When illuminated from the east, it casts a triangular shadow.

What is the shape of the actual object?

Equality Rules

How many equilateral triangles can you uncover in the pattern below?

Stop and Think

How many paths can lead you through the octagonal maze on the facing page? Before you begin, keep in mind that from start to finish, you can only move in the direction of the arrows.

There is a way to do this puzzle without tracing out each path. Can you discover the strategy?

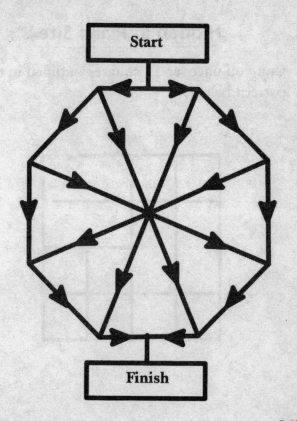

Start

Finish

263

Hidden in Plane Site

Can you uncover 15 squares outlined in the pattern below?

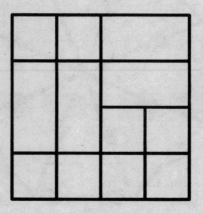

What's Your Sign?

The mathematical signs connecting the numbers below have been left out. Good thing we've supplied them on four tiles! Can you place the tiles between the numbers so that the final answer is 3? (All operations are done in left-to-right order.)

$$5 \ \blacksquare \ 2 \ \blacksquare \ 3 \ \blacksquare \ 5 \ \blacksquare \ 4 = 3$$

Controversial Cube

If you assume that the pattern below is the "outside" of the material, which two cubes on the facing page can be constructed by folding this pattern?

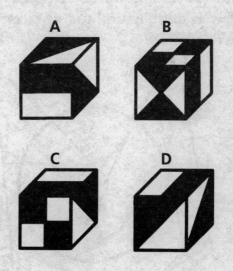

Gym Rat

Are the belts and wheels arranged to spin freely as this quizzical rodent races up the treadmill?

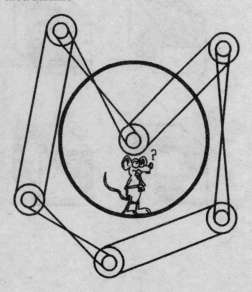

Sugar on the Side, Please

The owners of a local cafe have ordered coffee pots in two sizes. If coffee pot **A** holds about 8 ounces of tasty java, about how many ounces will it take to fill **B**?

Rack 'em Again ... and Again!

The billiard balls shown on the facing page are positioned in a six-ball rack. If you add the values of any three-ball edge, you will come up with 10.

Now, you've got to rearrange the billiard balls. Can you place them within this rack to produce three other patterns that also produce equal-sum sides?

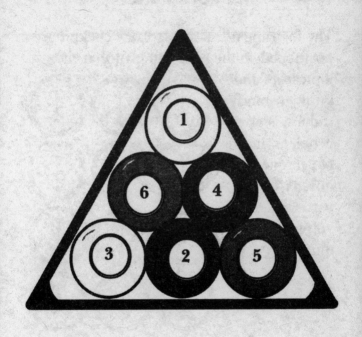

Pilot's Panel

The instruments in an aircraft's cockpit are positioned so the pilot can glance at the indicators and know instantly if there is a problem. In this panel, one dial doesn't fit the pattern. Can you locate it quickly?

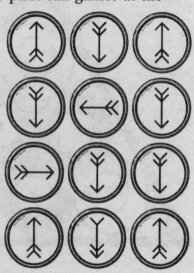

Table for Two

As these two lovebirds slurp up a shared piece of spaghetti, will a knot form in the pasta?

Black & White Rollups

If you rolled this pattern into a cylinder, which one of the choices on the facing page will it look like?

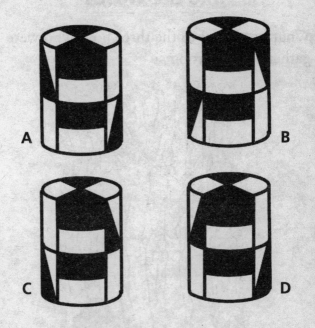

A B

C D

Into the Woods

What happened to the three boys who were gathering mushrooms?

End of the Line

Alas, the party is over, and the amusement park is closed. Even the roller-coaster ride is being sold.

The only thing left is the section of the track and frame shown below, and to be moved, it must be divided into identical parts. Can you do it?

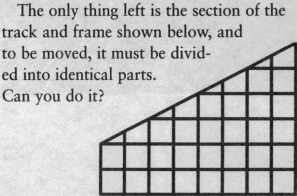

Answers
Answers
Answers
Answers
Answers
Answers
Answers
Answers
Answers
Answers

Page 7

It's both, of course. Concentrate on the white area and you'll see the vase. Concentrate on the black and the two men will appear.

Page 10

All five fields have exactly the same area. The different shapes make them appear to be different sizes.

Page 12

No. Both blocks are the same size. If they look unequal in size, it's because of the different black lengths on either side of them.

Page 13

If you figured that they're both the same size, you're correct!

You could be looking at the cube from above or below! Sometimes you will feel you're looking up at the cube from below, and sometimes you will feel you are looking down on the cube from above.

The line does seem to be slightly bent, but it isn't. It's perfectly straight!

Page 14

The diagonal line is quite straight. The vertical lines behind it make it seem distorted.

Page 17

The angles are the same! They **look** unequal because of the other angles on either side of them, which **are** different.

Page 21

Page 23	They're equal, but the titled square seems larger.
Page 24	All of these effects can be seen in this image.
Page 26	The circles spin to the right. Many people say the cogwheel turns to the left; others say it stands still.
Page 27	Top set: The large wheel will spin the same way as the smaller wheel. Bottom set: Top wheel moves clockwise, then reverses direction before completing a rotation.

The white square seems a little larger than the black square, but in fact, they're exactly the same size.

Page 28

All three are the same length. It is the **angles** that make the horizontal lines look like different lengths.

Page 34

Both lines are the same length. Once again, it is the angles the lines make that cause them to look unequal.

Page 35

This is one of those odd figures that you feel you are seeing from above at one moment and from below at the next. Whichever way you look at it, it's still confusing!

Page 36

Page 39

It's both. Look at the picture long enough and you'll see the old lady at one moment and the girl the next.

Page 42

If you said you saw the letter B, that's because you first perceived the vertical line of numbers, 12, 13, 14.

Page 44

Both circles are the same size. If they look different, it is because of their positions inside the angle.

Page 45

If you think you managed to find the top and bottom steps, you are wrong. They don't exist because this stairway is an impossibility!

They are **all** perfectly straight. It is the pattern of wavy lines behind them that makes them appear to bend.

Page 47

It looks greater, but in fact it's the same.

Page 48

Don't worry, your money's safe. No matter how skilled your friends may be in carpentry, they will never be able to build this crate. It's an **impossible object**.

Page 49

Both are exactly the same length. It's the difference in position that makes the lower one **look** longer.

Page 50

The answer is six or seven. It will be six if you saw the patterned part as the **top** of each cube, but seven if you saw the patterned part as the **bottom** of each cube.

The path out of the maze is shown here:

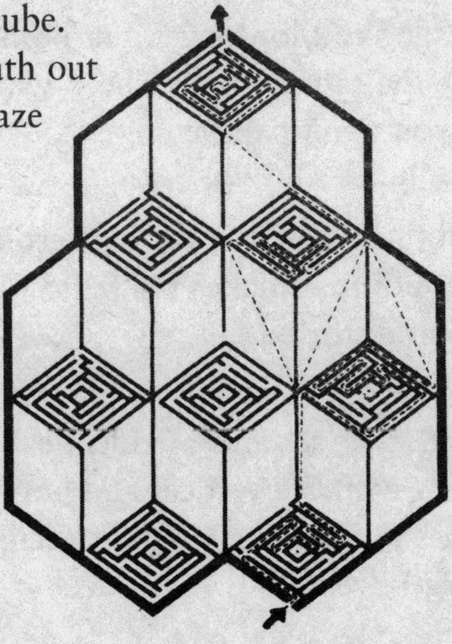

Page 58

You may be wrong! The one on page 59 certainly **looks** smaller, but in fact both circles are identical in size.

Page 63

AB **looks** a lot longer, but both lines are the same length. Check with a ruler if you don't believe it.

Page 64

All three are! It is the background pattern that makes the perfect circles seem distorted.

Page 66

The three squares are identical. The ones with the vertical and horizontal lines in them just seem to occupy a larger area.

The newspaper has 56 pages. Here's how the numbers are arranged on each double sheet.

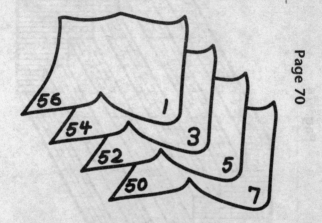

They don't bend at all! They are perfectly straight parallel lines.

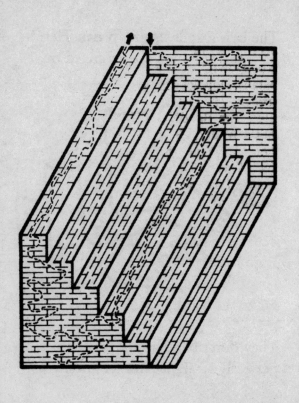

The two thin lines are of equal lengths.

Page 76

You can't do it! The wooden triangle is one of those "impossible objects."

Page 77

A looks a little larger than **B**, but both circles are the same size.

Page 78

Both horizontal lines are the same length. It's the converging lines that make the top line look longer.

Page 80

Both are possible. It depends on how you look at it.

Page 81

The height of the hat and the width of the brim are identical—vertical lines often seem longer than horizontal lines of the same length. Here's the solution to the maze:

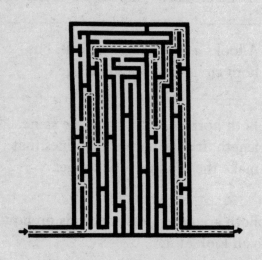

Never. This is a trick drawing—another "impossible object"!

Page 84

There's no way to tell. The twin with the horizontal stripes seems to be fatter, but he really isn't. Our eyes follow the lines in his suit, so the twin on the right seems broader and shorter than his brother.

Page 85

No, but it seems higher and wider in the back because of the way it has been drawn. We expect the back of the cube to be farther away and to look smaller. Since it is the same size, we automatically assume it is bigger in the back.

Page 86

1) Cut out an L-shaped section of the square like this:

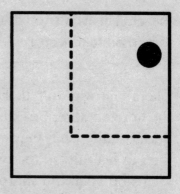

2) Rotate the cutout L-shape to the opposite corner of the piece with the hole.

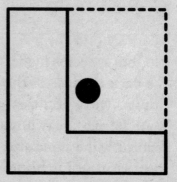

No, but it seems to be because **B** is in a larger area.

They are all the same height. The man at the right looks tallest. We expect things to look smaller when they are farther away. The man at the right is farthest away, and we would expect him to look the smallest. Since he doesn't, we assume he's really larger than the others.

The dot-shaped cross is just to the right of the center of the diagram. It spells out "R-I-G-H-T." It may take you a while to find it because the other dots distract your attention.

Nothing, except that the stripes make them look as if they are rocking back and forth. They are exactly parallel to each other.

Exactly parallel. The thicker cross-hatch lines just give the illusion that they are bending. Some scientists say this is because we can't judge the size of angles well. Others say the cross-lines distract us.

Yes, they run parallel to each other.

Either one, depending on where you place your attention. When you look at the **A** the dotted wall seems to be in front. When you look at the **B** it seems to be in back.

Page 96

It could be either one.

Page 97

Depending on the way you look at it, either side.

Page 98

Both. There are eight cubes with black tops, or seven cubes with white bottoms!

Page 99

Page 100	Either!
Page 101	Either one.
Page 102	The four detectives have equally large mouths.
Page 103	All the objects are the same length!

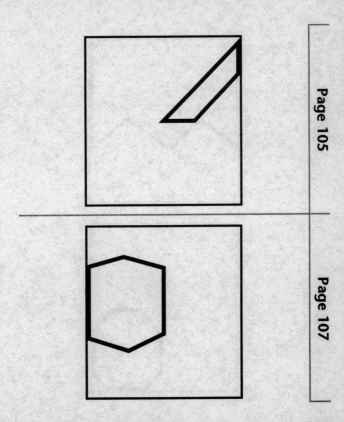

Page 105

Page 107

Page 109

Page 111

They are both the same height and width. The one with the horizontal stripes looks wider because your eyes follow the horizontal lines.

It is an exact square, but when it is broken by other lines, our eyes are distracted and follow the new lines instead of the original square.

Yes. The other lines distract from them and make them seem to bend a little, but they are parallel.

Page 116

Nothing. It is a perfect square, tipped on its side, but the distracting boxes make it seem warped.

Page 117

Yes.

Page 118

No. Our eyes cannot separate the figure from the intercepting arcs. Nevertheless, it is a perfect square.

Page 119

No, but the circle makes it look that way.

There is one exact square.

Page 120

Same.

Page 121

Absolutely nothing. It is an exact circle.

Page 122

No. It's a perfect circle.

Page 123

Page 125

They all sit on level ground.

Page 127

A triangle with equal sides.

Page 128

They are the same size. Scientists tell us that we still see the sky as a kind of flattened dome, nearer to us than the horizon—even though we know better. When any object is close to the horizon, we assume it is farther away than when it is overhead. Therefore, while the moon is always the same size, we trick ourselves into thinking that it is larger when it is near the horizon.

The inner circles are the same size, although the right circle looks smaller.

Page 130

They are all the same size.

Page 132

Page 133

In row **A** both circles are the same size, but the white one seems larger. When bright light falls on the retina of our eyes (where the nerve cells are), more nerve fibers react than actually had the light hit them. This causes a "spreading" effect, making the light object seem larger. In row **B** the black circle is actually larger, although both circles seem to be the same size.

Page 134

The curved lines force our eyes to move to the left of the true center, so try measuring the horizontal line with a ruler.

Page 136

You see gray dots at the point where white meets white. The white lines look brightest when they contrast with the black areas. When white meets white, they are less bright—and the gray dots appear.

Page 137

The vertical lines seem to lean to the right.

When you focus on the points where the lines cross, these vertical lines also appear to lean to the right.

As you turn the page or as your eyes tire, the overlapping images cause you to see "moiré" designs, like a plane's moving propeller, within the circle.

You see an even blacker lattice design inside the black squares! This is the result of your eyes being tired of seeing the white lines—so they record the black instead when you look away.

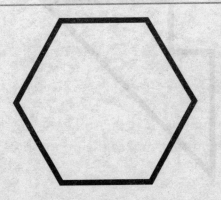

They are straight. Tilt this book all the way back and you'll have proof!

Clockwise, the distance between the lines seems to constrict. Counter-clockwise, the distances between the lines appear to expand.

Page 149

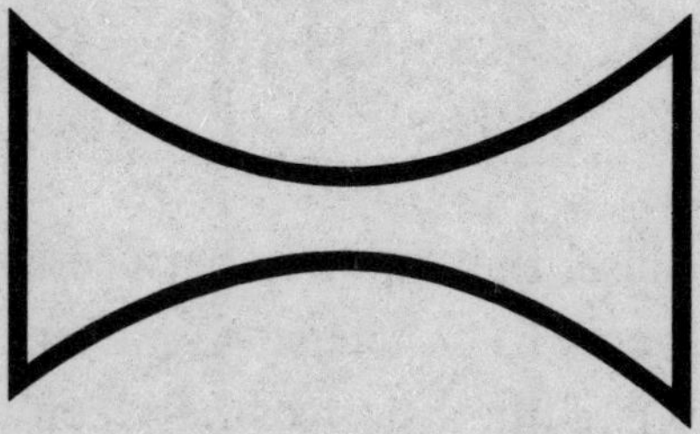

Page 150

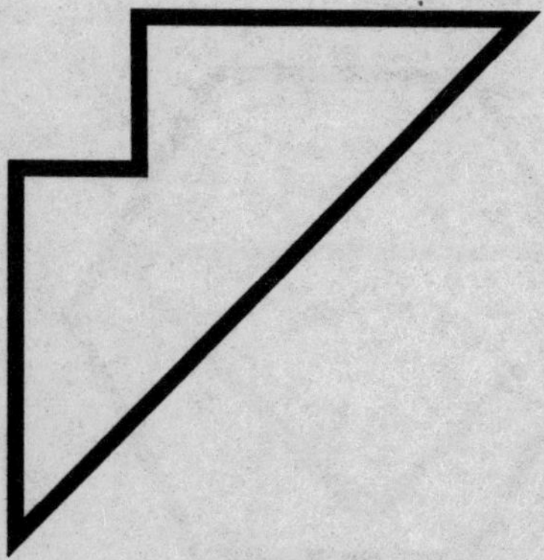

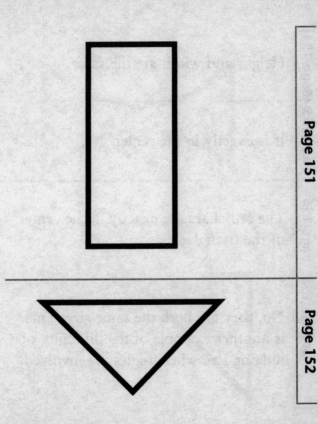

Page 151

Page 152

Page 154

Height and width are the same.

Page 155

It is exactly in the center.

Page 156

The crossbars are exactly in the center of the triangles.

Page 157

No, they are both the same size. This is another example of the difficulty of judging size when angles are involved.

Depending on how you focus on the letters, the staircase can run up from **A** to **B**—or you could be standing beneath the upside-down version. To see it upside down, focus on the **A**.

Page 158

Line **A** equals **B** and **C** equals **D**. Line **A** seems longer than **B** because we unconsciously add the circles on the end of the line to its length. The same is true of line **C** with its open square.

Page 159

The lines are the same length, but the vertical one seems longer. Some scientists say that the horizontal line looks shorter simply because it has been broken into two parts.

Page 160

They are the same.

The height of the tower is the same as the width of the church (including the base of the tower).

All the sides are the same length. The sides of C look longer because of the area they enclose.

Left: Yes, but when you break a straight line with a solid bar, the straight line seems displaced. Right: **B** is the continuation of **A**. **C** looks as though it connects with **A** because the solid bar "displaces" the line.

Page 164

In each figure, **A** equals **B**.

Page 165

The center lines in drawings **A** through **F** are all the same height. The only differences are the angles of the lines leading away from them.

Page 166

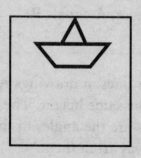

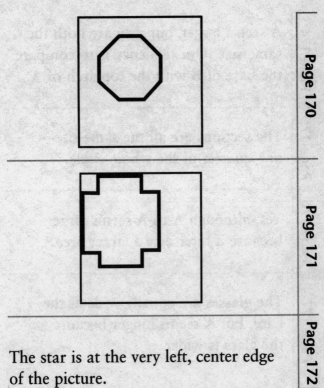

Page 170

Page 171

Page 172

The star is at the very left, center edge of the picture.

A seems larger, but they are both the same size. Our tendency is to compare the base of **B** with the top arch of **A**.

The sections are all the same size— one-quarter of the whole circle.

Yes, although **A**-to-**A** seems larger because it intersects a larger area.

The glasses are equally wide at the base, but **A** seems longer because the glass is wider.

The showman's wife is actually his dog! The dog's front legs form her legs, and the dog's fluffy tail forms her head.

The cat is hidden between the two left-hand branches of the tree.

The donkey is hidden between the two women.

The table is the cup! Its handle is formed by the back of the chair on the right-hand side.

The houses at the top of the picture are built on top of the giant's nose, and the small forest to the right forms his eyebrows. The enclosure near the middle of the picture forms his ear, and the large patch of forest forms his beard.

Turn the book upside down and you will see the land-lord's face on the far-left between the branches of the tree and the ground.

The butler's face is hidden in the dog's coat! If you turn the page upside-down, you'll see that the dog's shoulder is also

the butler's chin, and the butler's nose extends under the dog's arm.

One child's face is hidden in the top
of Mother Hubbard's hat. Another is
hidden upside-down in the shoe, just
above the tea tray. A third child's face
can be seen below Mother Hubbard's
shawl that wraps her shoulders, and
a fourth bulges out of her apron, just
below the bow tied around her waist.
The last child is hidden in the hem of
her apron!

The rats have hidden their faces in the cat's ears.

To find his master in the dog's face, turn the picture upside down. The man's

bearded face is hidden on the lower part of the dog's face (between his nose and eye), and his hat is formed by one of the faithful pet's ears.

Captain Webb's face is hidden in the cliff at the left of the picture, just below the pine trees.

The king has tumbled down behind her, with his head on the ground and his feet behind her head.

The tree behind the goat forms the milk-maid's hair. The goat's  tail and back leg form her profile.

The clever rabbit has hidden itself in the cook's hat on top of his head—the last place he would think to look for it.

In the left-hand corner of the picture, you'll find the hidden bird. Its beak and breast are defined by the outer curves of the two baskets, and its eye is the little bump on the side of the long stick.

Page 224

Fifteen handshakes. The first person would have shaken hands five times. The next person only needed to make four handshakes, since the handshake with one person had already been completed. The next person required only three, and so on. That gives us $5 + 4 + 3 + 2 + 1 = 15$.

Page 225

Page 226

Page 228

Just open the bottom link! The top two links are not attached to each other.

It's **9.** The numbers are obtained by adding the values of the two circles that are attached by diagonal lines. Then the value within the circle directly atop is subtracted from this sum. In the final grouping, it's 7 + 6 − 9, or 9.

It should be **27.** The number at the center of any circle is equal to the sum of the number located on its outline.

Page 233

The next number is 10. The sequence is formed by first doubling a number and then subtracting 1.

Page 234

Since they have the same number of teeth, they will spin at the same speed! Cog C does not affect the rate the teeth pass at; it only transfers the passage of teeth from cog B to cog D.

Page 235

The center hand in the bottom row is unlike the others. It alone is a right hand.

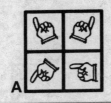

A

IV

III

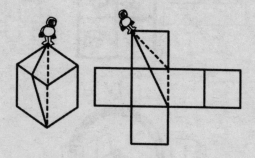

No! To visualize her path, let's undo the cube into its component faces. From this diagram, you can see that the shortest distance between two points is a straight line—which doesn't coincide with the path the astronaut planned.

Page 242

or

Page 244

Figure **B** is the solution.
Here's why:

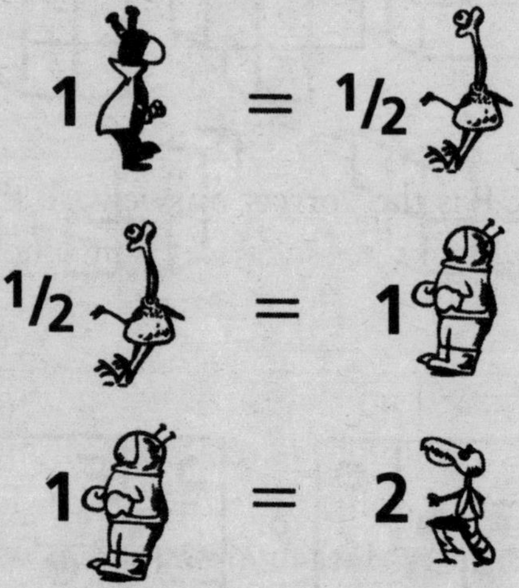

1 = 1/2

1/2 = 1

1 = 2

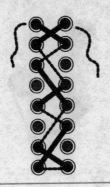

Page 248

Block **F** is the correct answer. All five other blocks are identical, but block **F** is a mirror image of those blocks.

Page 250

The final height of the stack approaches 2 feet. Although there are an infinite number of dolls, the size of each doll diminishes. Mathematically, that works out to 1 foot + $\frac{1}{2}$ foot + $\frac{1}{4}$ foot + $\frac{1}{8}$ foot + $\frac{1}{16}$ foot + $\frac{1}{32}$ foot ...

Page 252

Page 254

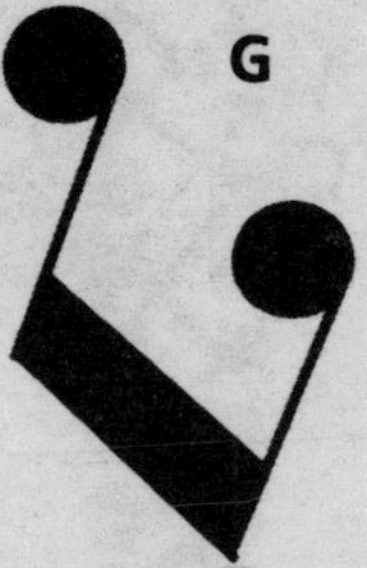

G

Page 255

Pencil # 7

Page 256

The string will come free of the pipe. Start at the pipe to visualize this action. From there, trace the pipe's path out from the center. After a few turns, the pipe exits freely at the opening on the right side of the maze.

C is the correct answer. The cube that's not shown is shaded in this diagram:

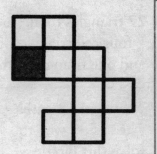

It is a cylinder that has been cut into a wedge! Two slices that extend from the upper diameter to opposite sides of the bottom have been removed to form this shape.

27 triangles total: 16 one-cell triangles, 7 four-cell triangles, 3 nine-cell triangles, and one triangle with 16 cells.

There are 18 paths. The easiest way to solve this puzzle is to start at the beginning and determine the number of paths that can get you to an intersection. The number of paths to each successive intersection is equal to the sum of the paths that are "attached" to it.

The 15 squares include:

One	4 x 4 square
Two	3 x 3 squares
Four	2 x 2 squares
Eight	1 x 1 squares

$$5 \boxtimes 2 \boxminus 3 \boxplus 5 \boxdiv 4 = 3$$

Cubes **A** and **D**

No, the belts are arranged in a pattern that doesn't allow them to move!

Coffee pot **B** holds about 4 ounces (half of pot **A**). The amount is determined by the height of the spout. The level cannot rise above the opening, because the extra coffee would spill out from the spout!

Here are the diagrams for three new patterns. The equal-side sums are 11, 12, and 9, respectively.

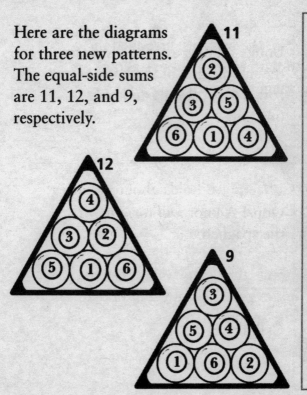

Page 272

Unlike all the rest, the arrow in the middle dial of the bottom row has two heads and only one tail!

Page 273

Oops! A knot *will* form in the spaghetti.

Page 274

Cylinder D

If you turn the page upside down, you'll find their faces nestled in the trees!

Page 276

Cut along this dotted line:

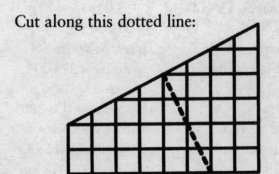

Page 277

Index

The page number for the puzzle title is followed by the page number for the answer in italic. Note: If there is no italicized number, the puzzles did not require separate answers.